The Comparative Morphology and Evolution of the Internal
Female Reproductive System of Trichoptera

The Comparative Morphology and Evolution of the Internal Female Reproductive System of Trichoptera

JOHN D. UNZICKER

ILLINOIS BIOLOGICAL MONOGRAPHS 40

UNIVERSITY OF ILLINOIS PRESS URBANA, CHICAGO, AND LONDON 1968

Board of Editors: Robert S. Bader, James E. Heath, Richard B. Selander, Hobart M. Smith, and Ralph S. Wolfe.

This monograph is a contribution from the Department of Entomology, University of Illinois. Issued August, 1968.

252 78405 7

Acknowledgments

This study was supported by a grant from the National Science Foundation. It formed the basis of a thesis submitted to the Graduate College of the University of Illinois in partial fulfillment of the requirements for the degree of Doctor of Philosophy in Entomology. The author would like to express his sincere thanks to Dr. Herbert H. Ross for his guidance throughout the course of this investigation. The author would also like to thank Dr. Oliver S. Flint, Jr. of the Smithsonian Institution and Dr. Glenn B. Wiggins of the Royal Ontario Museum for the loan of specimens.

CONTENTS

INTRODUCTION

During the routine clearing of female caddisfly abdomens for the purpose of specific identification the author noticed internal saclike structures which, after careful dissection, proved to be parts of the internal reproductive system. A number of authors have described this system for certain species of Trichoptera, and two have compared its structure in two or more species. A comparative morphological study throughout the order Trichoptera revealed a great amount of variability, led to the establishment of homologies between the various internal female reproductive organs in the different families of Trichoptera, and in turn led to an examination of this system in other orders of insects closely related phylogenetically in an attempt to establish homologies with the reproductive organs of these orders.

The question then arose as to how the internal female reproductive system of Trichoptera came to have the diverse forms it exhibits today. An examination of the different modifications of the internal female genitalic characters in the Trichoptera and other closely related orders resulted in establishing the probable ancestral and derived conditions of these characters.

Heretofore phylogenetic thinking about the Trichoptera has been based on external adult characters such as wing venation, mouth parts, leg spination, and genitalia, and external larval characters and behavior. An attempt is made here to trace the pattern of evolutionary development of the femal reproductive system and to see what insights into the phylogeny of the order might emerge from a study of the female genitalic characters in conjunction with recent ideas concerning the evolution of the Trichoptera.

MATERIALS

The following forty-seven species, representing three orders and twenty-nine families of insects, form the basis of this investigation. Twenty-six of the thirty-four families of Trichoptera recognized by Ross (1967) were studied. Material was unavailable for the following eight families which belong to the suborder Integripalpia: Thremmidae, Phryganopsychidae, Pisuliidae, Calocidae, Helicophidae, Philanisidae, Antipodoeciidae, and Philorheithridae.

Order Mecoptera
    Panorpidae
        Panorpa sigmoides Carpenter
Order Lepidoptera
   Suborder Jugatae
    Eriocraniidae
        Eriocrania sp.
   Suborder Frenatae
    Sphingidae
        Sphinx pinastri Latreille
Order Trichoptera
   Suborder Annulipalpia
    Psychomyiidae
        Psychomyia flavida Hagen
        Tinodes waeneri Linnaeus

Polycentropodidae
Neureclipsis crepuscularis (Walker)
Phylocentropus placidus (Banks)
Polycentropus crassicornis Walker
Dipseudopsidae
Dipseudopsis mirata Ross and Kingsolver
Stenopsychidae
Stenopsyche sp.
Hydropsychidae
Arctopsyche grandis (Banks)
Hydropsyche betteni Ross
Xiphocentronidae
Xiphocentron mexico Ross
Philopotamidae
Chimarra socia Hagen
Sortosa aequalis (Banks)
Suborder Integripalpia
Rhyacophilidae
Rhyacophila coloradensis Banks
Glossosomatidae
Glossosoma intermedium (Klapalek)
Hydroptilidae
Hydroptila hamata Morton
Rhynchopsychidae
Kokiria mirano McFarlane
Lepidostomatidae
Lepidostoma sp.
Lepidostoma togatum (Hagen)
Oeconesus maori McLachlan
Theliopsyche sp.
Limnephilidae
Limnephilus submonilifera Walker
Neothremma alicia Banks
Pycnopsyche subfasciata (Say)
Radema stigmatella (Zetterstedt)
Plectrotarsidae
Plectrotarsus gravenhorstii Kolenati
Goeridae
Goera calcarata Banks
Goerita genota Ross
Brachycentridae
Brachycentrus occidentalis Banks
Micrasema rusticum (Hagen)

Phryganeidae
  Phryganea cinerea Walker
  Yphria californica Banks
Limnocentropodidae
  Limnocentropus sp.
Leptoceridae
  Athripsodes tarsi-punctatus (Vorhies)
  Triaenodes florida Ross
Sericostomatidae
  Beraeoptera roria Mosely and Kimmins
  Olinga feredyi McLachlan
  Sericostoma personata Kirby
Pycnocentrellidae
  Pycnocentrella eruensis Mosely and Kimmins
Odontoceridae
  Marilia flexuosa Ulmer
Calamoceratidae
  Anisocentropus pyraloides (Walker)
  Notiomyia sp.
Helicopsychidae
  Helicopsyche borealis Hagen
Beraeidae
  Beraea fontana Wiggins
Molannidae
  Molanna uniophila Vorhies

METHODS

The internal reproductive organs and associated ducts are membranous and quite fragile or heavily sclerotized. Therefore it was necessary to use several different techniques in studying this organ system. In one method, live specimens were put in Bouin's picroformal fixing fluid; then the abdomen was detached and dissected to determine the shape, size, and relation of the ovaries and oviducts to the other internal organs, both genital and nongenital. The second method consisted in detaching the abdomen from the thorax and placing it in hot aqueous 10% potassium hydroxide solution for fifteen minutes. The abdomen was then transferred to a watch glass of distilled water where it remained for twenty-four hours. The potassium hydroxide treatment destroys the mesodermal cells, which form the paired ovaries and lateral oviducts, and leaves the ectodermal cells of the cuticle, which form the vagina, accessory glands, spermatheca, spermathecal gland, prespermathecal diverticulum, bursa copulatrix, and median oviduct. To facilitate the observation of the internal genital organs, in cases where the body wall was heavily sclerotized, the abdomen was opened on the pleuron from the first to ninth segments, and the sternites were peeled back, exposing the internal parts.

GENERAL FEATURES
OF THE FEMALE REPRODUCTIVE SYSTEM

Comparison with Lepidoptera and Mecoptera

Crampton (1929), Snodgrass (1933), and Ross (1965, 1967) give evidence that the neuropteroid orders of insects are closely related phylogenetically. Except for certain specializations (e.g., two genital openings in the specialized Lepidoptera, loss of the bursa copulatrix in some families of Coleoptera), the female genitalia of the neuropteroid insects are very similar, also suggesting a close relationship between these orders. The female members of these groups (excluding the lepidopteran suborder Jugatae) possess a single genital opening, the vulva, and a genital chamber or vagina into which open the accessory glands, spermatheca, bursa copulatrix, and median oviduct.

The genitalia of the Trichoptera, primitive Lepidoptera (Jugatae), and Mecoptera are associated with the ninth and tenth abdominal segments. As mentioned previously the female genitalia are basically the same in these three orders but differ in detail. The following is a discussion of the different organs of the female reproductive systems of these three groups plus the specialized Lepidoptera (Frenatae).

Vagina. The vagina (Vag) of Trichoptera, which opens externally between the ninth and tenth segments, is an elongate chamber with heavy muscular walls (Fig. 1A). Often one or more sclerotized elements are associated with the vagina internally (Figs. 7, 8, 10, and

11). The vagina of the primitive Lepidoptera is very similar to that of the Trichoptera in having a heavy muscular wall and associated internal sclerotized elements (Fig. 2). In the specialized Lepidoptera (Fig. 3) there are two genital openings. The anterior opening or vulva (Vul) serves as a copulatory opening and eggs are discharged through the posterior opening, or oviporus (Ovp). The vulva opens on the posterior part of the eighth abdominal segment and the oviporus on the posterior part of the ninth abdominal segment. The vulva communicates with the bursa copulatrix (Bcpx) in the specialized Lepidoptera. In the Trichoptera, primitive Lepidoptera, and Mecoptera the vulva communicates with the vagina. The vagina of Mecoptera is muscular and has associated sclerotized elements like those of the Trichoptera and primitive Lepidoptera, but differs in having a pair of anteriorly projecting sclerotized rods called spermathecal apodemes (Fig. 4A, Spt Apd).

Accessory Glands. The accessory glands (Ac Glds) of Trichoptera are elongate structures lying dorsal to the vagina between the ovaries (Fig. 1A). They open into the vagina dorsally and posteriorly through a common accessory gland duct (Fig. 7, Ac Gld D). In the primitive Lepidoptera the accessory glands may be tri-lobed (Fig. 2), but their position and point of insertion on the vagina are very similar to those of the Trichoptera. The accessory glands of the specialized Lepidoptera open into the vagina dorsally and posteriorly (Fig. 3). The accessory glands of Mecoptera may be a single pair of very long tubular structures which open into the vagina dorsally (Fig. 4A).

Spermatheca. The spermatheca (Spt) of Trichoptera lies above the vagina between the ovaries (Ov) and is generally an elongate membranous sac which opens into the vagina anteriorly to the accessory gland duct through a spermathecal duct (Spt D, Fig. 1A). The trichopteran spermatheca often has a spermathecal gland (Spt Gld). This gland is also present in the primitive and specialized Lepidoptera (Figs. 2 and 3) but is absent in the Mecoptera (Fig. 4A). A pre-spermathecal diverticulum (P Spt Div), which arises from the spermathecal duct, is present in some families of Trichoptera (Figs. 14, 21, and 22A). The author has not found this structure in the Lepidoptera, Mecoptera, or any other insect order which he examined. The spermathecae of the primitive and specialized Lepidoptera are elongate membranous sacs (Figs. 2 and 3) as in the Trichoptera. The spermathecal duct of the primitive Lepidoptera opens into the vagina dorsally and anteriorly to the accessory gland duct (Fig. 2) as in the Trichoptera, but in the specialized Lepidoptera (Fig. 3) it may open into the vagina ventrally as well as dorsally. The spermatheca of Mecoptera is also an elongate membranous sac (bean-shaped in the Panorpidae, Fig. 4A). The spermathecal duct enters the vagina anteriorly between the spermathecal apodemes.

Bursa Copulatrix. The bursa copulatrix of Trichoptera lies between the ovaries ventral to the spermatheca and is generally a single elongate membranous sac referred to as the primary sac (Fig. 1A, Bcpx) by the author. In some families of Trichoptera a second or accessory sac (Bcpx′), which arises from the primary sac, is present (Fig. 1A). The bursa copulatrix communicates with the vagina through a spermathecal duct which inserts dorsally at the anterior end of the vagina. In the primitive Lepidoptera the bursa copulatrix is an elongate membranous sac arising at the anterior end of the vagina (Fig. 2). Apparently only the primary bursal sac is present. The bursa copulatrix of the specialized Lepidoptera, like that of Trichoptera and primitive Lepidoptera, is an elongate membranous sac. It differs from these groups, however, in that it opens externally through the ductus bursa (D Bur, Fig. 3), not through the vagina. The bursa is connected to the vagina by the ductus seminalis (D Sem), not by the bursal duct as in the Trichoptera and primitive Lepidoptera. The bursa copulatrix of Mecoptera (e.g., Panorpidae) is a bi-lobed membranous sac opening into the vagina anteriorly and ventrally (Figs. 4A and B).

Median Oviduct. The ovaries (Ov), which are connected to ligaments (Lg) anteriorly, lie on either side of the mid- and hindgut. The two lateral oviducts (L Ovd) unite posteriorly to form the median oviduct (M Ovd, Figs. 1A and B). In the Trichoptera the median oviduct opens into the vagina anteriorly and ventrally (Figs. 1A and B). Its insertion is ventral to that of the bursa copulatrix. This same condition exists in the primitive Lepidoptera and the Mecoptera (Figs. 2 and 4A). In the specialized Lepidoptera the median oviduct opens into the vagina anteriorly, but the insertion may be dorsal (Fig. 3) or ventral.

Pattern in the Trichoptera

Several authors have described the internal female reproductive system of a number of species of Trichoptera. Stitz (1904) described the internal female reproductive system of *Phryganea striata* Curtis, *Leptocerus aterrimus* Stephens, *Hydropsyche guttata* Pictet, *Molanna angusta* Curtis, and *Limnephilus bipunctatus* Curtis. Deoras (1945) described the internal female genitalia of *Stenophylax, Anabolia, Hydropsyche, Rhyacophila, Mystacides,* and *Polycentropus,* and Korboot

(1964) described the internal female genitalia of *Triplectides volda* Mosely, *Anisocentropus latifasciata* (Walker), and *Cheumatopsyche modica* McLachlan. Denning (1943) has described the external female genitalic characters of several species in the genera *Hydropsyche*, *Cheumatopsyche*, *Potamyia* and *Macronemum*, and Gower (1967) has described the internal female genitalia of *Limnephilus lunatus* Curtis.

The internal female reproductive organs (Fig. 1) store the sperm, and produce, protect, nourish, and discharge the oocytes. The female reproductive system is derived from the two primary germ layers, the mesoderm and ectoderm. The ovaries (Ov), ovarial ligaments (Lg), and lateral oviducts (L Ovd) are believed to be mesodermal in origin, and the median oviduct (M Ovd), spermatheca (Spt), spermathecal gland (Spt Gld), spermathecal duct (Spt D), pre-spermathecal diverticulum (P Spt Div), bursa copulatrix (Bcpx, Bcpx'), accessory glands (Ac Glds), vagina (Vag), and vulva (Vul) are believed to be ectodermal in origin (Snodgrass, 1935).

The general organization of the trichopteran female reproductive system was discussed in the previous section, but some additional comments concerning variation of the different organs within the Trichoptera are in order. Generally the spermatheca is an elongate sac but it may be constricted or bi-lobed (Figs. 13, 14, and 24). The spermathecal gland is an elongate diverticulum which may arise anteriorly or ventrally from the spermatheca (Figs. 14, 22A, and 30). In some cases an enlarged section or reservoir is present (Fig. 30). The pre-spermathecal diverticulum is generally long and is often coiled around the reproductive organs. This diverticulum is present in all but two families of the suborder Integripalpia and absent in all of the families of the suborder Annulipalpia. In the families Dipseudopsidae (Fig. 12), Stenopsychidae (Fig. 1A), Philopotamidae (Figs. 17 and 18), and Glossosomatidae (Fig. 19) the bursa copulatrix is composed of a primary sac (Bcpx) and an accessory sac (Bcpx'). In all the other families only a primary sac is present. The bursa copulatrix is absent in the psychomyiid genus *Psychomyia* (Fig. 7). The accessory glands are elongate structures and may be composed of two single structures (Fig. 1A) or two tri-lobed structures (Fig. 44). A pair of sclerotized plates (Scl Plt) have been observed in the accessory gland duct of the genus *Sericostoma* (Sericostomatidae, Fig. 39B), and a single plate has been observed in the accessory gland duct of the genus *Anisocentropus* (Calamoceratidae, Fig. 46). The function of these plates is not known, but they may serve as valves to regulate the flow of accessory gland secretion into the vagina. No muscles have been observed attached to the spermatheca, accessory glands, pre-spermathecal diverticulum, or bursa copulatrix, and all of these organs have tracheoles ramifying over their surfaces externally.

In some families (e.g., Limnephilidae, Fig. 30), a pair of thickened lips (Vul) are associated with the genital opening, whereas in other families there are none (e.g., Xiphocentronidae, Fig. 16). Some female Trichoptera have an ovipositor similar to that of certain Diptera, Mecoptera, and Lepidoptera, in which the posterior abdominal segments can be telescoped to form a tube, but lack an ovipositor comparable to that of the Orthopteroid and Hemipteroid insects and the Hymenoptera, which is composed of valvifers and associated valves. The Polycentropodidae, Dipseudopsidae, and Hydropsychidae have six fleshy papillae (Pap, Fig. 6) on the tenth tergum which are directed posteriorly and are very likely sensory in function.

Many female caddisflies are not identifiable to species because of the paucity of diagnostic characters. The shape of the ninth and tenth abdominal tergites as well as the shape of the vagina (in species in which it is sclerotized) are generally used to separate species. Some species which lack a sclerotized vagina can be separated on the basis of the ninth tergite (e.g., clasper grooves in the genus *Hydropsyche*). This study has uncovered several internal female genital characters which may eventually be of use in separating species. In the genus *Lepidostoma*, for example, the shape of the spermatheca, presence of hairs or sclerotized plaques on the spermatheca, and the arrangement of the spermathecal chambers can be used to separate species (Figs. 15 and 17). Additional characters which are apparently diagnostic for genera have also been found. For example, in the genus *Theliopsyche*, a pair of small sclerotized plates present on the inside of the spermatheca (Fig. 16) is absent in the genus *Lepidostoma*.

In this study the interpretation of the homologies of the female genital organs of Trichoptera with those of Lepidoptera is based on Snodgrass (1935, Fig. 288), Bourgogne (1950, Figs. 1-5, and 1-7), Philpott (1927, Figs. 1, 9, 10, and 13-17), and Williams (1941, Figs. 1-15, and 1943). The point of insertion of the spermathecal gland, the spermatheca, accessory glands, bursa copulatrix, and median oviduct on the vagina, and the presence of sperm or spermatophores have been utilized as a basis for establishing homologies between organs.

The internal sac which initially receives the sperm in insects is generally considered the bursa copulatrix. In caddisflies the vagina, not the bursa copulatrix, receives the sperm initially. If the internal genital organs of Trichoptera, Mecoptera, and Lepidoptera are compared it is evident that the bursa copulatrix of Trichoptera is a sac arising at the anterior end of the vagina (Fig. 1A, Bcpx). This sac is called the "receptaculum seminis" by Stitz (1904), a "gland of un-known function" by Cholodkovsky (1913), the "spermatheca" by Deoras (1945), and the "pear-shaped gland" by Korboot (1964) and Khalifa (1949). The sperm or spermatophores pass from the vagina into a sac located dorsal to the bursa (Fig. 1A, Spt). This structure is referred to as the "bursa copulatrix" by Dodson (1935) and Khalifa (1949), and the "shell gland" by Deoras (1945). Dodson (1935) gives histological evidence purporting to show that the positions of the bursa and the spermatheca in Trichoptera are just the reverse of those in Lepidoptera. Thus in Trichoptera the bursa would be dorsal and the spermatheca ventral, and in Lepidoptera the spermatheca would be dorsal and the bursa ventral in postion. However, if these organs are examined it is apparent that the dorsal organ in Trichoptera has a spermathecal gland as does the dorsal organ in Lepidoptera and these organs are also utilized for sperm storage. It would seem then that the dorsal organ is the spermatheca and the ventral organ the bursa copulatrix.

The pre-spermathecal diverticulum, present in some families of cad-disflies, is designated as the "receptaculum seminis" by Cholodkovsky (1913), and Stitz (1904) and Dodson (1935) refer to this structure as the "flagellum." The families of Trichoptera which possess a pre-spermathecal diverticulum utilize this diverticulum for sperm storage (Dodson, 1935), and the families which do not possess this diverticu-lum utilize the dorsal sac or organ for sperm storage (Korboot, 1964). Thus it appears that the trichopteran spermatheca is actually two dis-tinct structures: (1) a dorsal sac with a spermathecal gland and (2) a diverticular tubule. These two structures are referred to in this paper as the spermatheca and pre-spermathecal diverticulum, respectively.

Development in the Trichoptera

Pictet (1834), Klapalek (1889), Vorhies (1905), and Dodson (1935) are of the opinion that the gonads appear in the larval stage just before pupation. Korboot's observations (1964) on three species of caddisflies indicate that the gonads first appear in the last larval instars, and ac-cording to Lübben (1904) the gonads are present in the early larval instars.

In *Brachycentrus subnubilus* Curtis (Dodson, 1935) the mesodermal tissues destined to form the ovaries and oviducts grow posteriorly from the anterior end of the fifth abdominal segment and meet the ectoder-mal invaginations destined to form the vagina, accessory glands, spermatheca, median oviduct, and bursa which grow anteriorly from the eighth and ninth abdominal sternites. The bursa copulatrix and spermatheca arise as dorsal unpaired outgrowths of the seventh segment, and the accessory glands as independent paired invaginations of the ninth sternum. When the larva undergoes metamorphosis, the internal genitalic organs increase in size, and the spermathecal gland and pre-spermathecal diverticulum appear. The organs are fully developed in the mature pupa and when the adult female emerges the oocytes increase in size, the female is inseminated, and fertilization occurs followed by oviposition.

In *Limnephilus lunatus* Curtis (Gower, 1967) females emerge in an immature state and maturation is slow. Gower divides maturation into four stages: A (newly emerged female), B (maturing female), C (mature female before oviposition) and D (mature female soon after oviposition). In the newly emerged female the fat body is well developed but the reproductive system is small. As maturation proceeds through steps B and C to D the bursa copulatrix, spermatheca, spermathecal gland, pre-spermathecal diverticulum and their associated ducts increase in size; the accessory glands increase in size and become distended with a viscous mucus secretion then are emptied and collapse; the oocytes develop within the ovarioles and are discharged; the fat body becomes reduced or absent; and the female is inseminated.

Function of the Reproductive Organs

After copulation, the sperm moves first to the spermatheca, and then to the pre-spermathecal diverticulum where it is stored until fertilization (Khalifa, 1949). In the families which do not have a pre-spermathecal diverticulum, the sperm is stored in the spermatheca until fertilization. Korboot (1964) has observed that it takes two days for the sperm to move from the vagina to the spermatheca in *Cheumatopsyche modica* (McLachlan), which lacks a pre-spermathecal diverticulum. The sperm are released through the spermathecal duct into the vagina where they fertilize the oocytes as the latter enter the vagina through the median oviduct.

The function of the trichopteran spermathecal gland is not known, but it may produce a secretion required for the maintenance of sperm. The spermathecal gland of Lepidoptera is secretory in function and is composed of rings of from twelve to fourteen large cuboidal secretory cells lining the central duct which have extremely large round nuclei (Callahan and Cascio, 1963). Khalifa (1949) has found a positive correlation between the length of the spermathecal gland in Trichoptera and the size of the protein mass of the spermatophore. The secretion produced by the accessory glands provides a gelatinous coating for the eggs which swells in water (Ross, 1944) and may serve to attach them to the substratum. The accessory glands usually lie below the hindgut, or when distended the glands lie on either side of the hindgut and above the ovaries. The function of the bursa in Trichoptera has not been thoroughly investigated, but Khalifa (1949) has found rod-shaped bacteria as well as motionless sperm in the bursa.

The sperm may be deposited in the vagina as a liquid mass or a spermatophore may be utilized. Spermatophores consisting of a coagulated protein mass and a sperm sac have been reported by Khalifa (1949) in the families Sericostomatidae (e.g., *Sericostoma personatum* Spence and *Silo nigricornis* Pictet), Molannidae (e.g., *Molanna angusta* Curtis), and Limnephilidae (e.g., *Halesus radiatus* Curtis, *Limnephilus politus* McLachlan, and *Anabolia nervosa* Durbis), by Korboot (1964) in the family Hydropsychidae (*Cheumatopsyche modica* McLachlan) and by Gower (1967) in the family Limnephilidae (*Limnephilus lunatus* Curtis). What may be spermatophores have been observed in the Lepidostomatidae (e.g., *Lepidostoma* sp. and L. *togatum*, Figs. 23 and 24). In *Sericostoma, Silo,* and *Molanna* the entire spermatophore is deposited in the spermatheca and the neck of the sperm sac is held in position by a cuticular calyx at the posterior end of the spermatheca. In *Anabolia* and other limnephilids the protein mass of the spermatophore is deposited in the spermatheca while the sperm sac is placed in the spermathecal duct. In *Anabolia* the protein mass is completely absorbed after nine to ten days (Khalifa, 1949). Sclerotized rings (Fig. 32B) probably homologous to Khalifa's cuticular calyx have been observed in the spermathecal ducts and mouth of the spermatheca (e.g., *Lepidostoma, Radema, Goera, Beraea,* and *Helicopsyche*). These rings may serve to hold the sperm sac in position inside the spermatheca (Sp S, Figs. 23 and 24). A pair of small sclerotized plates bearing hooks on the inside of the spermatheca of *Theliopsyche* (Fig. 22A) probably serve a similar function.

Caddisfly mating behavior can be roughly divided into two parts: (1) the mating flight, usually over water at dusk, and (2) copulation, usually on vegetation overhanging the water's edge. The arrangement of the male and female genitalic structures during copulation can be determined by examining the cleared abdomens of specimens which have been collected while mating. Figure 6 shows the male (stippled) and female (unstippled) genitalic structures of *Hydropsyche walkeri* Betten and Mosely during copulation. The male ninth abdominal segment forms a sclerotized ring or annulus which is fused with the tenth abdominal segment. The ninth segment has a pair of lateral sclerotized triangular flaps (Scl Flp). Dorsally the tenth segment is produced into a pair of sclerotized lobes (Scl Lb) and ventrally articulates with a pair of two-segmented claspers (Clsp) or inferior appendages. The aedeagus lies between the claspers inside the ring formed by the fused ninth and tenth segments. The aedeagus is attached to the posterior part of the tenth segment by a membranous sheet and internally by a ligament (Lg). When fully extruded, the base of the aedeagus lies inside the ninth and tenth segments, and the distal portion in the vagina.

The female vaginal opening is located posteriorly and ventrally between the ninth and tenth segments. The ninth abdominal segment forms a sclerotized ring and is continuous with the tenth tergum which is membranous and bears three pairs of fleshy papillae. The ninth tergum has a pair of lateral pockets or clasper grooves (Clsp Grv). During copulation the distal part of the aedeagus is inserted into the vagina, and the ninth and tenth male abdominal terga are pushed up under the female ninth and tenth abdominal terga. The clasper tips are inserted into the clasper grooves and the basal part of the claspers is held in a groove between the lateral triangular flaps of the male ninth segment and the lateral part of the ninth tergum (Fig. 6). In this manner the claspers serve to hold the male and female together during copulation. The membranous lobes and associated sclerotized elements of the aedeagus, when expanded, may also serve to hold the mating pair together during copulation (Fig. 5). Denning has described the alignment of male and female genitalic structures for *Cheumatopsyche speciosa* (Banks) in copulo and it is very similar to that described above for H. *walkeri*.

Females of other species of the genus *Hydropsyche* as well as a number of species of the genus *Cheumatopsyche* have clasper grooves. Denning has shown that these grooves, which he subdivides into clasper groove and clasper receptacle, are valuable in separating species in these genera. Denning has also shown that there is a close correspondence between the length and width of the groove and the length and width of the male apical clasper segment. Thus in a species in which the female has a long narrow clasper groove, the male apical clasper segment is long and thin. This could be considered a type of "lock and key" mechanism which serves to prevent males and females of sympatric species from mating as well as a mechanism to hold the male and female together during copulation. The author has found no similar correspondence between the shape of the female vagina and the tip of the aedeagus.

COMPARATIVE MORPHOLOGY
OF THE TRICHOPTERAN FAMILIES

The following are descriptions of the internal female reproductive systems of the different families of Trichoptera based on an examination of selected genera.

PSYCHOMYIIDAE

The vagina of *Psychomyia* (Fig. 7) is a sclerotized tube (indicated by crosshatching). It communicates by way of a short spermathecal duct with the spermatheca, which has a long narrow neck with a bulbous enlargement at its anterior end. A bursa copulatrix is absent. The accessory gland duct communicates with the vagina dorsally to the median oviduct. In *Tinodes* (Fig. 8) the muscular vagina has a distinct sclerotized plate (crosshatched). Anteriorly the vagina narrows and then expands into a small round chamber. The long spermathecal duct connects with a spermatheca which is composed of two sacs. The ventral sac opens into the dorsal sac at its posterior end. The bursa copulatrix is a medium-sized round primary sac. The accessory gland duct opens into the vagina dorsally and posteriorly to the median oviduct.

POLYCENTROPODIDAE

The vagina of *Neureclipsis* (Fig. 9) communicates with a football-shaped spermatheca through a long spermathecal duct. The bursa

copulatrix is a large elongate primary sac which narrows at its posterior end communicating with the vagina through a short spermathecal
duct. The accessory gland duct communicates with the vagina dorsally
and posteriorly to the median oviduct. The vagina of *Phylocentropus*
(Fig. 10) has a sclerotized plate (crosshatched) extending its length.
The long spermathecal duct, which is slightly enlarged throughout its
length, communicates with a spermatheca consisting of a single round
sac. The bursa copulatrix is an elongate primary sac and opens into
the vagina via a short duct. The accessory gland duct communicates
with the vagina dorsally and posteriorly to the median oviduct. In
Polycentropus (Fig. 11) the vagina has a sclerotized ring located at
its anterior end. The spermathecal duct passes through this ring into
the vagina. The spermathecal duct is slightly expanded about one-
third its length from the vagina. The spermatheca is elongate and
tubular for about three-fourths of its length and then expands into a
round chamber. The bursa copulatrix is a large round primary sac.
The accessory gland duct opens into the vagina dorsally and posteriorly
to the median oviduct.

DIPSEUDOPSIDAE

In *Dipseudopsis* (Fig. 12) the vagina has an internal sclerotized
plate extending its length. The long spermathecal duct communicates
with a football-shaped spermatheca. The bursa copulatrix is composed
of an elongate primary sac and an even longer dorsal accessory sac
arising near its posterior end. The accessory gland duct opens into
the vagina dorsally and posteriorly to the median oviduct.

STENOPSYCHIDAE

The vagina of *Stenopsyche* (Fig. 1) is tubular. The accessory glands
are elongate paired structures and communicate with the vagina via a
short duct which is dorsal and posterior to the opening of the median
oviduct into the vagina. The spermathecal duct is a long, tightly coiled
duct which opens into a lobate C-shaped spermatheca. The bursa
copulatrix is an elongate primary sac with a large accessory sac arising
dorsally at its posterior end. The accessory gland duct opens into the
vagina dorsally and posteriorly to the median oviduct.

HYDROPSYCHIDAE

In the genus *Arctopsyche* (Fig. 15) the vagina has a large sclerotized
plate. The short spermathecal duct connects with a C-shaped lobate

spermatheca. The bursa copulatrix is a large elongate primary sac. The accessory gland duct opens into the vagina dorsally and posteriorly to the median oviduct. The vagina of *Hydropsyche* (Fig. 13) has a sclerotized ventral arm which communicates with the bursal duct. The spermatheca is a large elongate constricted sac extending most of the length of the abdomen. The bursa copulatrix is a medium-sized round sac. The accessory gland duct opens into the vagina dorsally and posteriorly to the median oviduct.

XIPHOCENTRONIDAE

The tubular vagina of *Xiphocentron* (Fig. 16) is lightly sclerotized dorsally. It is connected to the large elongate spermatheca by a short spermathecal duct. The accessory gland duct opens into the vagina dorsally and anteriorly to the median oviduct. Abdominal segments eight and nine have a pair of lateral sclerotized rodlike apodemes.

PHILOPOTAMIDAE

In the genus *Chimarra* (Fig. 17) the vagina has a sclerotized ring at its anterior end through which the spermathecal duct passes. The long spermathecal duct opens into a medium-sized dorsally bi-lobed spermatheca. A bi-lobed spermathecal gland arises from the anterior end of the spermatheca. The bursa copulatrix is a large primary sac with a small accessory sac arising ventrally near its posterior end. The vagina of *Sortosa* (Fig. 18), like that of *Chimarra*, has a sclerotized ring at its anterior end. The spermathecal duct is moderately long and enlarged for about half of its length, and communicates with a round saclike spermatheca. The bursa copulatrix is composed of a narrow elongate primary sac and a large elongate accessory sac arising dorsally near its posterior end. The accessory gland duct opens into the vagina dorsally and posteriorly to the median oviduct.

RHYACOPHILIDAE

The vagina of *Rhyacophila* (Fig. 14) has a sclerotized ring at its anterior end. A short pre-spermathecal diverticulum is present and arises from the spermathecal duct adjacent to the spermatheca. The spermathecal gland is short and arises at the anterior end of the spermatheca. The bursa copulatrix is a small round primary sac. The accessory gland duct opens into the vagina dorsally and posteriorly to the median oviduct. Abdominal segments eight and nine possess a pair of lateral sclerotized rodlike apodemes.

GLOSSOSOMATIDAE

In the genus *Glossosoma* (Fig. 19) the vagina has no sclerotized elements. The long spermathecal duct has an enlarged area which contains a small sclerotized ring; and the duct communicates with a large elongate spermatheca. The bursal duct has a small swelling near the vagina, and the bursa copulatrix is a large elongate primary sac with a medium-sized round accessory sac arising ventrally at its anterior end. The accessory gland duct opens into the vagina dorsally to the median oviduct. Abdominal segments eight and nine have a pair of lateral sclerotized rodlike apodemes similar to those found in the Rhyacophilidae.

HYDROPTILIDAE

The vagina of *Hydroptila* (Fig. 20) has a sclerotized ring (crosshatched) at its anterior end. The spermathecal duct is short and the spermatheca is an elongate sac. The bursa copulatrix is a medium-sized round primary sac. The accessory gland duct opens into the vagina dorsally to the median oviduct. Abdominal segments eight and nine have a pair of lateral sclerotized rodlike apodemes like those in the Rhyacophilidae and Glossosomatidae.

LEPIDOSTOMATIDAE

The vagina of *Lepidostoma* (Figs. 23 and 24) has a distinct sclerotized plate. The spermathecal duct is short and a pre-spermathecal diverticulum arises from the duct just before it opens into the spermatheca. *Lepidostoma* sp. has a short diverticulum and *L. togatum* has a moderately long diverticulum. The spermatheca of *Lepidostoma* sp. is an elongate sac with a small sclerotized cone-shaped structure at its posterior end and a series of small sclerotized placques at the anterior end. The anterior half, up to the placques, is covered with numerous tiny hairs. The spermatheca of *L. togatum* is a large laterally bilobed structure. Three-fourths of the length of the larger chamber is covered with single hairs which grade to double and triple at the posterior end. *L. togatum* has a long spermathecal gland but *L.* sp. lacks it. Both species of *Lepidostoma* which were examined have sperm sacs inside the spermathecae. These can be seen as small round structures with a narrow neck and an opening on one side (Sp S, Figs. 23 and 24). The bursa copulatrix of this genus is a medium-sized round or pear-shaped primary sac. In both species the accessory gland ducts open into the vagina dorsally and posteriorly to the median oviducts. In *Theliopsyche* (Fig. 22A) the vagina has a large sclerotized plate and the spermathecal duct is short. A long pre-spermathecal diverticulum arises from the enlarged anterior end of the spermathecal duct. The spermatheca is a large elongate chamber with a pair of small internal sclerotized plates bearing curved hooks which are located dorsally near its posterior end (Figs. 22A and B). The bursa copulatrix is a small round primary sac. The accessory gland duct opens into the vagina dorsally and posteriorly to the median oviduct.

The vagina of *Oeconesus* (Fig. 41) has a large round arched sclerotized plate. The spermathecal duct opens into the vagina through an opening in this plate. A pre-spermathecal diverticulum arises from the spermathecal duct near its insertion on the vagina. The spermatheca is a large elongate sac with a long spermathecal gland arising ventrally near its anterior end. The bursa copulatrix is a medium-sized round primary sac. The accessory gland duct opens into the vagina dorsally and posteriorly to the median oviduct.

LIMNEPHILIDAE

The vaginas of *Pycnopsyche* (Fig. 30), *Limnephilus* (Fig. 28), *Radema* (Fig. 31), and *Neothremma* (Fig. 29) have distinct sclerotized elements. A long pre-spermathecal diverticulum, which arises from the spermathecal duct, is present in all of these genera. In *Pycnopsyche* the posterior one-fourth of the spermatheca is small and is separated from the large elongate anterior part by a constriction. The spermatheca of *Limnephilus* is a large elongate chamber or sac and has a moderately long spermathecal gland arising ventrally at its posterior end. The spermatheca of *Radema* is a single large chamber which narrows abruptly anteriorly and ends at a small sclerotized ring. The short spermathecal gland arises from the spermatheca ventrally near the middle. The spermatheca of *Neothremma* is an elongate sac with a spermathecal gland arising from it ventrally near the anterior end. The spermatheca of *Pycnopsyche* is a large elongate chamber for two-thirds of its length and then narrows abruptly for the last one-third of its length. The spermathecal gland is small in diameter at its insertion on the spermatheca, but expands into a larger reservoir for almost half its length and then narrows again. The bursa copulatrices of these genera are medium-sized round primary sacs. In *Radema*, *Pycnopsyche*, and *Neothremma* the accessory gland duct opens into the vagina dorsally and posteriorly to the median oviducts. In *Limnephilus* this duct opens dorsally and anteriorly to the median oviduct. In *Drusus annulatus* Steph. (Gower, 1967) the accessory glands possess only a single pair of posterior lobes in contrast to the two pairs recorded in other

Limnephilids. Gower (1967) has described the internal female reproductive system of *Limnephilus lunatus* Curtis and his description is in
close agreement with the author's description of *Limnephilus submonilifera*.

PLECTROTARSIDAE

The vagina of *Plectrotarsus* (Fig. 34) has three distinct sclerotized
plates. The short spermathecal duct communicates with an elongate
spermatheca. A pre-spermathecal diverticulum arises from the spermathecal duct approximately half way between the vagina and spermathecal gland arises from the spermatheca at its anterior end and is
a short blind tube. The bursa copulatrix is a medium-sized round primary sac. The accessory gland duct opens into the vagina dorsally and
posteriorly to the median oviduct.

GOERIDAE

In the genera *Goera* (Figs. 32A and B) and *Goerita* (Fig. 33) the
vagina has a distinct sclerotized plate or tube through which the spermathecal ducts pass. Both genera have a long pre-spermathecal diverticulum arising from the spermathecal duct near the spermatheca. The
spermatheca of *Goera* is an eliptical sac with a small sclerotized ring
at its posterior end. A moderately long spermathecal gland arises from
the anterior end of the spermatheca. The spermatheca of *Goerita* is a
large elongate sac which has a short lobate spermathecal gland arising
at its anterior end. The bursa copulatrices of both genera are round
primary sacs. The accessory gland ducts of both genera open into the
vagina dorsally and posteriorly to the median oviduct.

BRACHYCENTRIDAE

The anterior half of the vagina of *Brachycentrus* (Fig. 26) contains
a sclerotized plate through which the spermathecal duct passes. In
Micrasema (Fig. 27) the vagina has a large sclerotized plate. Both
genera have a pre-spermathecal diverticulum with that of *Brachycentrus* being larger in diameter and shorter than that of *Micrasema*. The
spermatheca of *Brachycentrus* is a medium-sized sac with a short spermathecal gland arising at its anterior end. The spermatheca of *Micrasema* is a large elliptical sac with a spermathecal gland arising
ventrally half way between the anterior and posterior ends. Both
genera have an enlarged bursal duct. The bursa copulatrices of both
of these genera are round primary sacs. The accessory gland ducts of

Brachycentrus and *Micrasema* open into the vaginas dorsally and posteriorly to the median oviduct.

RHYNCHOPSYCHIDAE

In *Kokiria* (Fig. 25) the vagina has a large ringlike sclerotized plate at its anterior end. The spermathecal duct passes into the vagina through this ringlike plate. A moderately long rigid pre-spermathecal diverticulum arises from the spermathecal duct approximately half way between its insertion on the vagina and spermatheca. The anterior half of the spermathecal duct is enlarged and opens into a large elongate spermatheca. The spermathecal gland arises from the spermatheca ventrally near the anterior end. The middle two-fourths of the spermatheca is covered with short hairs externally. The bursa copulatrix is a single round primary sac. The accessory gland duct opens into the vagina dorsally and posteriorly to the median oviduct.

PHRYGANEIDAE

In the genus *Phryganea* (Fig. 35) the vagina has a small sclerotized ringlike plate at its anterior end. The vagina of *Yphria* (Fig. 36) has a large sclerotized plate. In *Yphria* the short spermathecal duct opens into the vagina through a small hole in the sclerotized plate. The pre-spermathecal diverticulum arises from the spermathecal duct approximately half way between the vagina and spermatheca. The spermatheca is a large elongate sac covered with short hairs on its outer surface. The spermathecal gland arises from the spermatheca ventrally toward the anterior end and is expanded distally to form a bifurcate chamber. In *Phryganea,* as in *Yphria,* the spermathecal duct opens into the vagina through the sclerotized plate. A long convoluted pre-spermathecal diverticulum arises from the spermathecal duct approximately half way between the vagina and spermatheca. The spermatheca of *Phryganea* is a large elongate sac which narrows just before it opens into the spermathecal duct. The long spermathecal gland arises from the spermatheca ventrally toward the anterior end. The bursa copulatrix is a round primary sac. In both genera the accessory gland duct opens into the vagina dorsally to the median oviducts.

LIMNOCENTROPODIDAE

The vagina of *Limnocentropus* (Fig. 37) has a sclerotized ring at its anterior end. The spermathecal duct opens into the vagina through this ring. The pre-spermathecal diverticulum arises from the spermathecal duct nearer the spermatheca than the vagina. A small sclerotized ring is located in the spermathecal duct just before it opens into the spermatheca. The spermatheca is a small elongate sac. A spermathecal gland is absent. The bursa copulatrix is a medium-sized round primary sac. The accessory gland duct opens into the vagina dorsally and ventrally to the median oviduct.

LEPTOCERIDAE

The vagina of *Athripsodes* (Fig. 21) contains two sclerotized plates. The ventral plate is U-shaped and the spermathecal duct opens into the vagina through this plate. The small dorsal plate is located just posterior to the accessory gland duct. The short spermathecal duct has a pre-spermathecal diverticulum arising from it approximately half way between the vagina and spermatheca. The spermatheca of *Athripsodes* consists of an elongate saclike structure with a narrow tubular posterior half and a round anterior half. A short spermathecal gland arises from the anterior end of the spermatheca. The short bursal duct opens into a medium-sized bursa copulatrix which is composed of a teardrop-shaped primary sac. The accessory gland duct opens into the vagina dorsally and anteriorly to the median oviduct. The vagina of *Triaenodes* (Fig. 49) has a U-shaped sclerotized plate very similar to that of *Athripsodes*. The small dorsal plate present in *Athripsodes* is lacking in *Triaenodes*. A long convoluted pre-spermathecal diverticulum arises from the spermathecal duct about midway between the vagina and spermatheca. The spermatheca of *Triaenodes* is an elongate sac which has a slight constriction near its anterior end. The spermathecal gland is a short lobate structure which arises from the spermatheca laterally near the anterior end. The bursa copulatrix is a medium-sized round primary sac. The accessory gland duct opens into the vagina dorsally and posteriorly to the median oviduct.

SERICOSTOMATIDAE

The vagina of *Sericostoma* (Figs. 39A and B) contains three plates: a long ventral plate, a small round central plate, and a medium-sized dorsal plate. The spermathecal duct opens into the vagina through a small hole in the ventral plate. A pre-spermathecal diverticulum arises from the spermathecal duct near its insertion on the spermatheca. The proximal end of the pre-spermathecal diverticulum is enlarged to form a reservoir-like chamber. The spermatheca of *Sericostoma* is a medium-sized elliptical sac. A spermathecal gland arises from the spermatheca ventrally just anterior to its midpoint. The bursa copulatrix is a large round primary sac. The accessory gland duct opens into the vagina dorsally and posteriorly to the median oviduct. The accessory gland duct contains a pair of distinct sclerotized plates (Scl Plt) located at its proximal end (Fig. 39B), each of which possesses a series of small finger-like lobes. These plates and lobes could possibly serve to regulate the flow of accessory gland secretion into the vagina. They were not found in any of the other caddisflies examined.

The vagina of *Olinga* (Fig. 42) contains a large ring-shaped sclerotized structure at its anterior end. The spermathecal duct opens into the vagina through a hole in this ring-shaped structure. A pre-spermathecal diverticulum arises from the spermathecal duct near its insertion on the vagina. The spermatheca is a large elongate sac which is constricted at its posterior end. The spermathecal gland is inserted on the spermatheca ventrally near its midpoint and is shaped like an inverted helmet. The bursa copulatrix is a round primary sac. The accessory gland duct opens into the vagina dorsally to the median oviduct.

In the genus *Beraeoptera* (Fig. 43) the vagina has a ring-shaped sclerotized structure similar to that of *Olinga*. The spermathecal duct opens into the vagina through a hole in this structure. A pre-spermathecal diverticulum arises from the spermathecal duct approximately half way betweeen the vagina and spermatheca. The spermatheca is an elongate sac and lacks a spermathecal gland. The bursa copulatrix is a round primary sac and the accessory gland duct opens into the vagina dorsally and posteriorly to the median oviduct.

PYCNOCENTRELLIDAE

In *Pycnocentrella* (Fig. 40) the vagina has a large circular sclerotized plate at its anterior end. The spermathecal duct opens into the vagina through a small hole in this plate. A long convoluted pre-spermathecal diverticulum arises from the spermathecal duct near its insertion on the vagina. The spermatheca is a large elongate sac. A small lobate spermathecal gland arises from the spermatheca ventrally anterior to its midpoint. The bursa copulatrix is a round primary sac. The accessory gland duct opens into the vagina dorsally to the median oviduct.

ODONTOCERIDAE

The vagina of *Marilia* (Fig. 44) contains a round sclerotized plate. The spermathecal duct opens into the vagina through a hole in this plate. A long convoluted pre-spermathecal diverticulum arises from the spermathecal duct just anterior to its midpoint. The spermatheca is a medium-sized round sac and lacks a spermathecal gland. The bursa copulatrix is a small round primary sac. The accessory gland duct opens into the vagina dorsally and posteriorly to the median oviduct. Each accessory gland is composed of an elongate lobe and two short triangular lobes near the posterior end.

CALAMOCERATIDAE

The vagina of *Anisocentropus* (Fig. 46) has a large arched sclerotized plate. The accessory gland duct contains a sclerotized plate (located dorsally) just before it opens into the vagina (Scl Plt). This plate may be homologous to one of the plates in the accessory gland duct of *Sericostoma* (Fig. 39B). The short spermathecal duct opens into the vagina through a hole in the vaginal plate. The spermatheca is a large teardrop-shaped sac and does not have a spermathecal gland. A long convoluted pre-spermathecal diverticulum arises from the spermathecal duct. The bursa copulatrix is a large round primary sac. The accessory gland duct opens into the vagina dorsally and posteriorly to the median oviduct.

In *Notiomyia* (Fig. 47) the vagina has a long sclerotized plate. The spermathecal duct opens into the vagina through a hole in this plate. A long convoluted pre-spermathecal diverticulum arises from the spermathecal duct about half way between the vagina and spermatheca. The spermatheca is a large elongate sac and does not have a spermathecal gland. The bursa copulatrix is a round primary sac. The accessory gland duct opens into the vagina dorsally and posteriorly to the median oviduct.

HELICOPSYCHIDAE

The vagina of *Helicopsyche* (Fig. 48) contains a large sclerotized plate. The spermathecal duct communicates with the vagina through a hole in this plate. The pre-spermathecal diverticulum arises from the spermathecal duct near the vagina. The spermatheca is a small elongate sac with a sclerotized cone-shaped cap (crosshatched) at its posterior end. No spermathecal gland is present. The bursa copulatrix has a large round primary sac and the accessory gland duct opens into the vagina dorsally and anteriorly to the median oviduct.

BERAEIDAE

The vagina of *Beraea* (Fig. 38) contains a large sclerotized plate which extends most of its length. The spermathecal duct opens into the vagina through a hole in this plate. The pre-spermathecal divertic-

ulum arises from the spermathecal duct near the vagina. The spermatheca is elongate and has a constriction in the middle which divides it
into a tubular posterior half and an elongate anterior half. There is a
sclerotized ring at the posterior end of the spermatheca and the spermathecal duct opens into the spermatheca through this ring. The bursa
copulatrix is a medium-sized round primary sac. The accessory gland
duct opens into the vagina dorsally to the median oviduct.

MOLANNIDAE

In *Molanna* (Fig. 45) the vagina contains a sclerotized plate which
is located at its anterior end. The spermathecal duct opens into the
vagina through this plate. A long convoluted pre-spermathecal diverticulum is present and arises from the spermathecal duct near the
vagina. The spermatheca is an elongate sac with a spermathecal gland
arising from its anterior end. The spermathecal gland is composed of
two finger-like lobes which open into a reservoir which in turn opens
into the spermatheca through a short narrow duct. The bursa copulatrix is a round primary sac and the accessory gland duct opens into
the vagina dorsally and slightly posteriorly to the median oviduct.

EVOLUTIONARY CONSIDERATIONS

The different modifications (i.e., conditions) of the bursa copulatrix, spermatheca, pre-spermathecal diverticulum, and spermathecal gland have been examined in an attempt to discover which are ancestral and which are derived for the Trichoptera.

Bursa copulatrix. The bursa copulatrix may be (1) present as a single primary sac (e.g., Fig. 10), (2) present as a primary sac with accessory sac (e.g., Fig. 12), or (3) absent (e.g., Fig. 7). An examination of this organ in other orders of insects indicates that in a number of these orders only the primary sac is present. This sac is present in some families of related orders and absent in other families of these same orders. Within the Trichoptera the bursa copulatrix is absent in the family Psychomyiidae. An accessory sac apparently occurs only in the Trichoptera. It seems probable therefore that the primary sac alone was present in the trichopteran ancestor and that the accessory sac and absent conditions are derived.

Spermatheca. The trichopteran spermatheca is generally an elongate sac (Fig. 7) but may be constricted (Figs. 13 and 14) or bi-lobed (Fig. 24). When it is compared with that of other insect orders it is apparent that a number of different spermathecal types have arisen independently in the Trichoptera and in other insect orders. Since there is no type common to the Trichoptera and other orders of insects, it is impossible to determine the ancestral condition of the spermatheca for the Trichoptera.

Pre-spermathecal diverticulum. The pre-spermathecal diverticulum has been found only in the Trichoptera and probably represents a derived condition peculiar to certain families of Trichoptera.

Spermathecal gland. The spermathecal gland occurs in the Lepidoptera and sporadically in the Trichoptera and probably represents a structure that evolved in the ancestor common to the Trichoptera and Lepidoptera but was subsequently lost several times in the former order. This conclusion is based on the assumption that, in the absence of evidence to the contrary, it is more reasonable to assume that the trichopteran ancestor possessed this structure than to assume that it was not present in this ancestor but arose independently in the Trichoptera and in the Lepidoptera.

Based on the inferences given above, it seems highly probable that the trichopteran ancestor exhibited the following combination of characters: bursa copulatrix composed of a primary sac, pre-spermathecal diverticulum absent, and spermathecal gland present.

The following are the derived conditions of the female genitalic characters: bursa copulatrix lost or composed of primary and accessory sacs, pre-spermathecal diverticulum present, pre-spermathecal diverticulum lost, and spermathecal gland lost.

An important question concerning the evolution of the female reproductive system is whether the derived conditions of the female genitalic characters arose one or more times. An examination of the distribution of these derived conditions among the families of Trichoptera in conjunction with Ross's phylogenetic diagram of the Trichoptera (1967, Fig. 1), which is based on both adult and larval anatomical characters and larval behavioral characters, may shed some light on this question.

Bursa copulatrix. The bursa copulatrix is absent only in the genus *Psychomyia* of the family Psychomyiidae (Fig. 7). It seems that here is a case of specialization through the simple loss of a structure. This loss has apparently occurred only once in the Trichoptera.

The accessory sac occurs in four families, the Stenopsychidae, Dipseudopsidae, Philopotamidae, and Glossosomatidae. This shared condition would seem to indicate that these families arose from an immediate common ancestor. However, an examination of the bursa copulatrix in these families (Figs. 1, 12, and 17-19) indicates that the primary bursal sacs are homologous on the basis of their insertion on the vagina, but the accessory sacs may not be homologous because they arise from the primary sac in different positions. If the adult and larval anatomical characters and larval behavior are considered, it is apparent that the Stenopsychidae, Dipseudopsidae, and Philopotamidae share several derived conditions (e.g., apical palpal segment annulate, supratentorium lost, and larvae net makers) with the families of the Annulipalpia, and thus they all probably arose from the same ancestor (ancestor 2, Fig. 50). The Glossosomatidae share several derived conditions with the families of the Integripalpia (e.g., larval ninth tergum sclerous, and larvae case makers), and apparently arose from the same ancestor (ancestor 5) as these families. This additional evidence would seem to indicate that the accessory sac condition has arisen independently at least four times in the Trichoptera.

Spermathecal gland. The spermathecal gland has been lost in a number of the families of both the suborder Annulipalpia and the suborder Integripalpia (Fig. 50).

In the Annulipalpia the spermathecal gland has been lost in the Stenopsychidae, Xiphocentronidae, Psychomyiidae, Polycentropodidae, Dipseudopsidae, and Hydropsychidae. An examination of the adult and larval anatomical characters (Ross, 1967, Fig. 1) in conjunction with the presence or absence of the spermathecal gland indicates that this gland was probably independently lost two times in the evolution of the Annulipalpia. An inspection of the derived conditions of the nongenitalic characters indicates that ancestor 2 split into two lines. In one line, which eventually gave rise to the Philopotamidae and Stenopsychidae, the larval head became elongate. Sometime after this line gave rise to these two families the spermathecal gland was apparently lost in the Stenopsychidae (Fig. 50).

The second line that arose from ancestor 2 (Fig. 50) subsequently gave rise to the remaining five families of the Annulipalpia. All these families share several derived characters (e.g., ocelli and Y-suture lost) which they did not share with the Stenopsychidae and Philopotamidae. This indicates that all five families very likely arose from an immediate common ancestor (ancestor 3). Since these families do not have a spermathecal gland it is highly probable that this gland was lost in the evolution of the Annulipalpia sometime after ancestor 3 arose from ancestor 2 (Fig. 50). An explanation which postulates the loss of this gland only once in the evolution of the Annulipalpia must conclude that the derived conditions of three nongenitalic characters have evolved more than once. The explanation cited here seems more probable because it proposes two losses and no multiple evolution of derived conditions of nongenitalic characters.

In the suborder Integripalpia the spermathecal gland was lost in two families of the superfamily Rhyacophiloidea (the Glossosomatidae and Hydroptilidae), and in seven families of the superfamily Limnephiloidea (the Sericostomatidae, Limnocentropodidae, Beraeidae, Sericostomatidae, Odontoceridae, Helicopsychidae, and Calamoceratidae) (Fig. 50).

An examination of the larval behavioral and anatomical characters of the Rhyacophilidae, Glossosomatidae, and Hydroptilidae indicates a stepwise development in the evolution of the larval tube-case making habit in the Rhyacophiloidea (Ross, 1967, Fig. 1). The larvae of Rhyacophilidae are free-living while those of the Glossosomatidae make saddle cases. In the early instars the larvae of the Hydroptilidae are free-living and in the late instars make purse or tube cases like those of the Limnephiloidea. Associated with the behavioral transition from a free-living ancestral condition to a tube-case making derived condition is a shift in postion of the larval anal legs from ventral to lateral and the addition of accessory teeth to these legs for anchoring the larva in its case. Thus there is good evidence to indicate that the Rhyacophilidae, Glossosomatidae, and Hydroptilidae arose from different immediate ancestors. The Rhyacophilidae probably arose from an ancestor with a free-living larva (ancestor 5), the Glossosomatidae from an ancestor with a larva which built a saddle case (ancestor 6), and the Hydroptilidae from an ancestor with a larva which was free-living in the early instars and a purse- or saddle-case maker in the late instars (ancestor 7). Since the spermathecal gland has been lost in the families Glossosomatidae and Hydroptilidae it seems highly probable that this gland was independently lost in the Glossosomatidae after they arose from ancestor 6, and in the Hydroptilidae after they arose from ancestor 7 (Fig. 50).

All the larvae of the families comprising the superfamily Limnephiloidea are tube-case makers with laterally directed anal legs for anchoring the larva in its case. Six of the families which arose from ancestor 8 lost the spermathecal gland (Fig. 50). In the limnephilid branch this gland was lost in the families Lepidostomatidae (only in *Lepidostoma* sp.) and Limnocentropodidae. Both of these families have derived conditions (e.g., male front wing with vein M4 lost, and larval pronotum with preapical crease) in common with other families of this branch, which suggests that they all arose from ancestor 8 (Ross, 1967, Fig. 1). Since there is also good evidence from nongenitalic characters to indicate that within this limnephilid branch these two families arose from different ancestors it is highly probable that the spermathecal gland has been lost independently two different times in the evolution of this branch.

In the leptocerid branch the spermathecal gland was lost in the families Beraeidae, Sericostomatidae, Odontoceridae, Helicopsychidae, and Calamoceratidae. These six families share several derived conditions (e.g., ocelli lost and supratentorium reduced) with the other families of the leptocerid branch, which suggests that all these families arose from a common ancestor (ancestor 8). Within the leptocerid branch further specializations occurred resulting in the evolution of five groups (ancestors 14-18). Since there is evidence for the separate evolution of these groups (Ross, 1967), it seems highly probable that the spermathecal gland was lost independently six times in the families which arose from these groups. An explanation which postulates a single loss of this gland in the evolution of the leptocerid branch must assume that a number of derived nongenitalic conditions arose more than once.

The foregoing evidence indicates that the spermathecal gland was lost independently at least two times in the evolution of the Annulipalpia and nine times in the evolution of the Integripalpia.

Pre-spermathecal diverticulum. The pre-spermathecal diverticulum is absent in all of the families of the suborder Annulipalpia but only in two of the families of the Integripalpia (the Glossosomatidae and Hydroptilidae). Since the trichopteran ancestor (ancestor 1) presumably did not have a pre-spermathecal diverticulum and since it is present in all but two families of the Integripalpia it probably first appeared in the line which gave rise to ancestor 5 (Fig. 50). As mentioned in the previous section, there is good evidence, from an examination of the nongenitalic characters, to indicate that the Glossosomatidae and Hydroptilidae arose from ancestors 6 and 7, respectively. Since this is apparently the case, the pre-spermathecal diverticulum was probably independently lost twice, once in the Glossosomatidae, and once in the Hydroptilidae.

The trichopteran pre-spermathecal diverticulum is generally long and coiled, but in the family Rhyacophilidae it is short and uncoiled. On the basis of changes in nongenitalic characters the Rhyacophilidae may be considered the most ancestral lineage of the Integripalpia, and therefore the short uncoiled condition may represent an intermediate stage in the evolution of the pre-spermathecal diverticulum between the ancestral absent condition and the derived long coiled condition. The family Lepidostomatidae, which represents a derived lineage of the Integripalpia, also has a short uncoiled pre-spermathecal diverticulum (Fig. 23). This may represent a retention of the short uncoiled condition or a reduction from the long coiled condition.

SUMMARY

The internal female reproductive systems of forty-four species, representing twenty-six families, of Trichoptera are described incorporating new information with that from previous studies. The development and function of the female reproductive system are discussed. Several characters have been discovered which may prove helpful in separating genera and species difficult or impossible to separate at present. Two species of the genus *Lepidostoma*, for example, can be separated on the basis of the shape of the spermatheca, presence or absence of an accessory sac, and presence or absence of sclerotized placques or hairs on the spermatheca. A pair of lateral internal sclerotized plates present in the spermatheca of *Theliopsyche* is apparently not present in the genus *Lepidostoma* and may be a useful character for separating these two genera as well as other genera of Lepidostomatidae.

The internal female genital organs of Trichoptera and other closely related orders are homologized. The following conditions were probably present in the trichopteran ancestor: bursa copulatrix composed of a primary sac, pre-spermathecal diverticulum absent, and spermathecal gland present. The following conditions are probably derived: bursa copulatrix composed of a primary and accessory sac, bursa copulatrix absent, pre-spermathecal diverticulum present, pre-spermathecal diverticulum absent, and spermathecal gland absent. An attempt is made to determine if these derived conditions arose more than once during the evolution of the Trichoptera by examining the changes in the female genitalic characters in conjunction with recent ideas concerning the phylogeny of the Trichoptera (Ross, 1967) based on changes in nongenitalic characters. The following changes probably occurred: (1) the accessory sac arose at least four times, (2) the bursa copulatrix was lost at least once, (3) the spermathecal gland was lost at least eleven times, (4) a pre-spermathecal diverticulum arose once, and (5) the latter was lost at least twice.

LITERATURE CITED

Bourgogne, J. 1950. L'Appereil genital femelle de quelques Hepialidae (Lépidopteres). Bull. Soc. Zool. France 74: 284-291.

Byers, G. W. 1954. Notes on North American Mecoptera. Ann. ent. Soc. Amer. 47(3): 484-510.

Callahan, P. S., and T. Cascio. 1963. Histology of the reproductive tracts and transmission of sperm in the corn earworm, *Heliothis zea*. Ann. ent. Soc. Amer. 56(4): 535-556.

Cholodkovsky, N. A. 1913. Ueber den Geschlechtsapparat du Trichopteren. St. Petersburg Trav. Soc. Nat. 1: 91-98.

Crampton, G. C. 1929. The terminal abdominal structures of female insects compared throughout the orders from the standpoint of phylogeny. Jour. N.Y. ent. Soc. 37: 453-496.

Denning, D. G. 1943. The Hydropsychidae of Minnesota. Ent. Amer. 23(3): 101-171.

Deoras, P. J. 1945. On the comparative morphology and evolution of the adult Trichoptera. Pt. II. Internal morphology. Indian Jour. Ent. 6: 35-48.

Dodson, M. E. 1935. Development of the female genital ducts in Trichoptera. Quart. Jour. micr. Sci. (n.s.) 77(307): 383-403.

Eidmann, H. 1929. Morphologische und phyliogische Untersuchungen am weiblichen Genitalapparat der Lepidopteren. I. Morphologischer Teil. Z. Angew. Ent. 15: 64 pp.

Gower, A. M. 1965. The life cycle of *Drusus annulatus* Steph. (Trich., Limnephilidae) in watercress beds. Ent. mon. Mag. 101: 133-141.

————. 1967. A study of *Limnephilus lunatus* Curtis (Trichoptera: Limnephilidae) with reference to its life cycle in watercress beds. Trans. Royal ent. Soc. Lond. 119(10): 282-302.

Khalifa, A. 1949. Spermatophore production in Trichoptera and some other insects. Trans. Royal ent. Soc. Lond. 100: 449-471.

Klapalek, F. 1889. The metamorphosis of *Apatoenia muliebris* McLachlan. A chapter in parthenogenesis. Ent. mon. Mag. 24: 241-242.

Korboot, K. 1964. Comparative studies of the internal anatomy of three species of caddisflies (Trichoptera). Univ. Queens. Pap. 2(1): 3-44.

Lübben, H. 1907. Ueber die innere Metamorphose der Trichopteren. Zool. Jb. 24: 71-128.

Philpott, A. 1927. Notes on the female genitalia of Micropterygoidea. Trans. Royal ent. Soc. Lond. 75: 319-323.

Pictet, F. J. 1834. Recherches pour servir à l'histoire et l'anatomie des Phryganides. Geneva: Abraham Cherbuliez. 255 pp.

Potter, E. 1938. The internal anatomy of the order Mecoptera. Trans. Royal ent. Soc. Lond. 87: 467-502.

Ross, H. H. 1944. The caddisflies or Trichoptera of Illinois. Bull. Ill. nat. Hist. Surv. 23(1): 326 pp.

————. 1965. A textbook of entomology. 3rd. ed. New York: John Wiley and Sons, Inc. 539 pp.

————. 1967. The evolution and past dispersal of the Trichoptera. Ann. Rev. Ent. 12: 169-206.

Snodgrass, R. E. 1933. Morphology of the insect abdomen. Pt. II. The genital ducts and the ovipositor. Smithson. misc. Coll. 85(6): 148 pp.

————. 1935. Principles of insect morphology. New York: The Macmillan Co. 667 pp.

Stitz, H. 1904. Zur Kenntniss des Genitalapparatus der Trichopteren. Zool. Jb. Anat. 20: 277-314.

Vorhies, C. T. 1905. Habits and anatomy of the larvae of the caddisfly *Platyphylax designatus* Walk. Trans Wis. Acad. Sci. Arts Lett. 15: 232-235.

Williams, J. L. 1941. The relations of the spermatophore to the female reproductive ducts of Lepidoptera. Ent. News. 52: 61-65.

————. 1943. The internal genitalia and mating behavior of *Eurukuttarus confederata* Grt. Jour. Morph. 72: 601-611.

GLOSSARY

Ac Glds	Accessory glands	Ovp	Oviporus
Ac Gld D	Accessory gland duct	Pap	Papillae of tenth tergum
Aed	Aedeagus		
Apd 8	Apodeme of eighth abdominal segment	P Spt Div	Pre-spermathecal diverticulum
Apd 9	Apodeme of ninth abdominal segment	Rect	Rectum
		S 7	Sternum 7
Bcpx	Primary sac of bursa copulatrix	S 8	Sternum 8
		Scl Flp	Sclerotized flap
Bcpx'	Accessory sac of bursa copulatrix	Scl Lb	Sclerotized lobe
		Scl Plt	Sclerotized plate
Bcpx D	Duct of bursa copulatrix	Sp S	Sperm sac of spermatophore
Clsp	Clasper	Spt	Spermatheca
Clsp Grv	Clasper groove	Spt Apd	Spermathecal apodeme
Cr	Cercus		
Cr B	Cercal base	Spt D	Spermathecal duct
D Bur	Ductus bursa	Spt Gld	Spermathecal gland
D Sem	Ductus seminalis	Vag	Vagina
Lg	Ovarial ligament	Vul	Vulva
Lg'	Aedeagal ligament	T 7	Tergum 7
L Ovd	Lateral oviduct	T 8	Tergum 8
M Ovd	Median oviduct	T 9	Tergum 9
Ov	Ovaries	T 10	Tergum 10

PLATE 1

Fig. 1. Stenopsychidae, *Stenopsyche* sp., A: left lateral aspect of female genitalia, B: dorsal aspect of lateral and median oviducts, C: dorsal aspect of accessory glands and accessory gland duct.

Fig. 2. Lepidoptera, Eriocraniidae, *Eriocrania* sp., left lateral aspect of female genitalia.

Fig. 3. Lepidoptera, Sphingidae, *Sphinx pinastri*, left lateral aspect of female genitalia (modified from Eidmann, 1929).

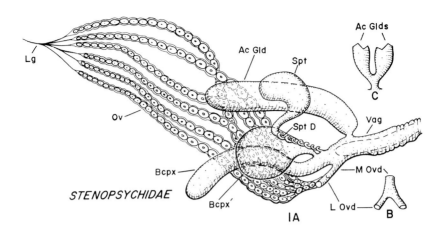

STENOPSYCHIDAE

IA

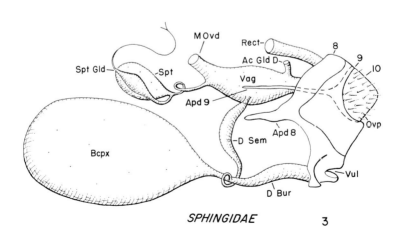

ERIOCRANIIDAE

2

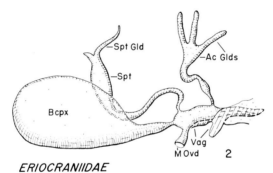

SPHINGIDAE

3

PLATE 2

Fig. 4. Mecoptera, Panorpidae, *Panorpa sigmoides,* A: left lateral aspect of female genitalia, B: ventral aspect of bursa copulatrix.

Fig. 5. Male and female of *Hydropsyche walkeri* in copulo, left lateral aspect of vagina, and right lateral aspect of end of aedeagus.

Fig. 6. Male and female of *Hydropsyche walkeri* in copulo, right lateral aspect of female genitalia, and left lateral aspect of male genitalia.

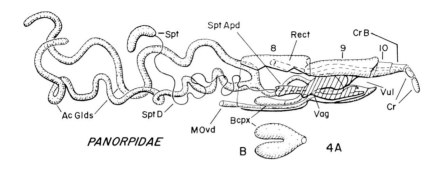

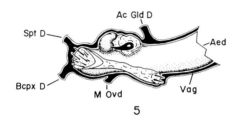

PANORPIDAE

4A

5

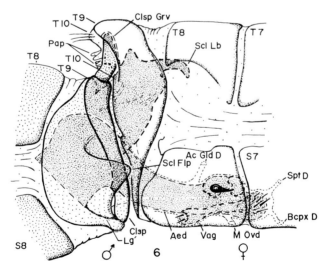

6

PLATE 3

Fig. 7. Psychomyiidae, *Psychomyia flavida*, left lateral aspect of female genitalia.

Fig. 8. Psychomyiidae, *Tinodes waeneri*, left lateral aspect of female genitalia.

Fig. 9. Polycentropodidae, *Neureclipsis crepuscularis*, left lateral aspect of female genitalia.

Fig. 10. Polycentropodidae, *Phylocentropus placidus*, left lateral aspect of female genitalia.

Fig. 11. Polycentropodidae, *Polycentropus crassicornis*, left lateral aspect of female genitalia.

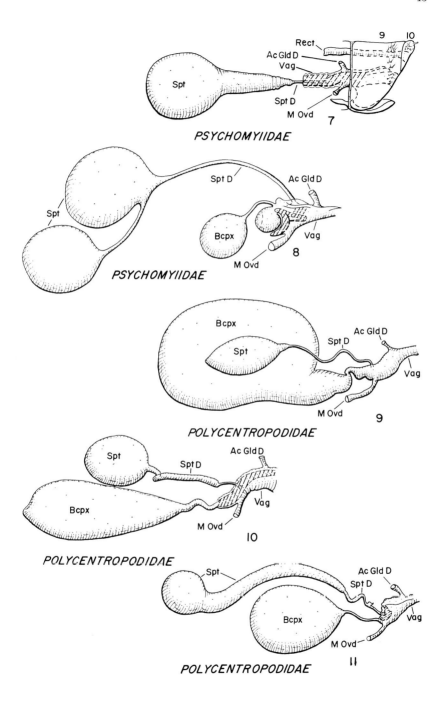

PSYCHOMYIIDAE

PSYCHOMYIIDAE

POLYCENTROPODIDAE

POLYCENTROPODIDAE

POLYCENTROPODIDAE

PLATE 4

Fig. 12. Dipseudopsidae, *Dipseudopsis mirata*, left lateral aspect of female genitalia.

Fig. 13. Hydropsychidae, *Hydropsyche betteni*, ventral aspect of female genitalia.

Fig. 14. Rhyacophilidae, *Rhyacophila coloradensis*, ventral aspect of female genitalia.

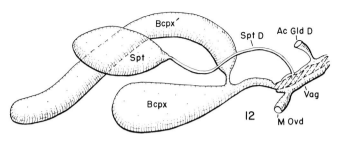

DIPSEUDOPSIDAE

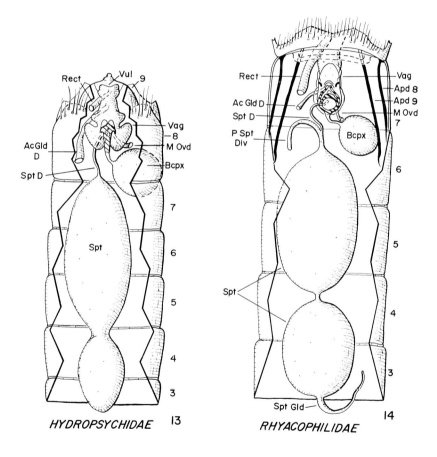

HYDROPSYCHIDAE

RHYACOPHILIDAE

PLATE 5

Fig. 15. Hydropsychidae, *Arctopsyche grandis*, left lateral aspect of female genitalia.

Fig. 16. Xiphocentronidae, *Xiphocentron mexico*, left lateral aspect of female genitalia.

Fig. 17. Philopotamidae, *Chimarra socia*, left lateral aspect of female genitalia.

Fig. 18. Philopotamidae, *Sortosa aequalis*, left lateral aspect of female genitalia.

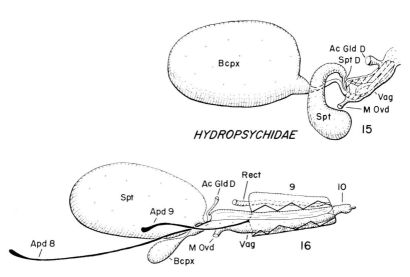

HYDROPSYCHIDAE 15

XIPHOCENTRONIDAE

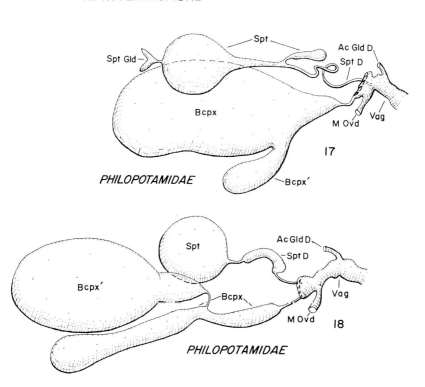

PHILOPOTAMIDAE 17

PHILOPOTAMIDAE 18

Plate 6

Fig. 19. Glossosomatidae, *Glossosoma intermedium,* left lateral aspect of female genitalia.

Fig. 20. Hydroptilidae, *Hydroptila hamata,* left lateral aspect of female genitalia.

Fig. 21. Leptoceridae, *Athripsodes tarsi-punctatus,* left lateral aspect of female genitalia.

Fig. 22. Lepidostomatidae, *Theliopsyche* sp., A: left lateral aspect of female genitalia, B: sclerotized plate of spermatheca.

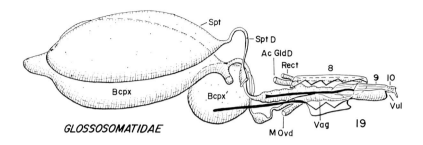

GLOSSOSOMATIDAE

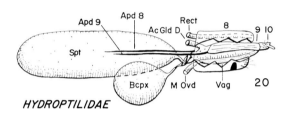

HYDROPTILIDAE

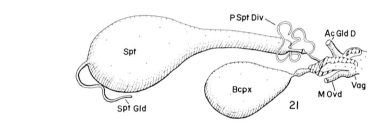

LEPTOCERIDAE

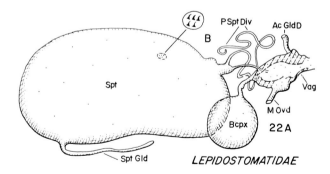

LEPIDOSTOMATIDAE

PLATE 7

Fig. 23. Lepidostomatidae, *Lepidostoma* sp., ventral aspect of female genitalia.

Fig. 24. Lepidostomatidae, *Lepidostoma togatum,* ventral aspect of female genitalia.

Fig. 25. Rhynchopsychidae, *Kokira minaro,* left lateral aspect of female genitalia.

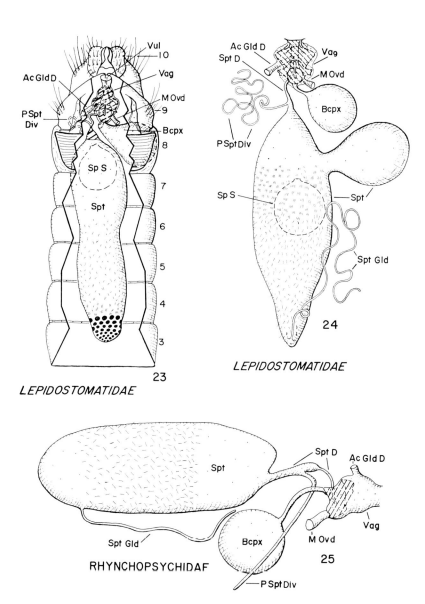

LEPIDOSTOMATIDAE
23

LEPIDOSTOMATIDAE
24

RHYNCHOPSYCHIDAF
25

52

Fig. 26. Brachycentridae, *Brachycentrus occidentalis*, left lateral aspect of female genitalia.

Fig. 27. Brachycentridae, *Micrasema rusticum*, left lateral aspect of female genitalia.

Fig. 28. Limnephilidae, *Limnephilus submonilifera*, left lateral aspect of female genitalia.

Fig. 29. Limnephilidae, *Neothremma alicia*, left lateral aspect of female genitalia.

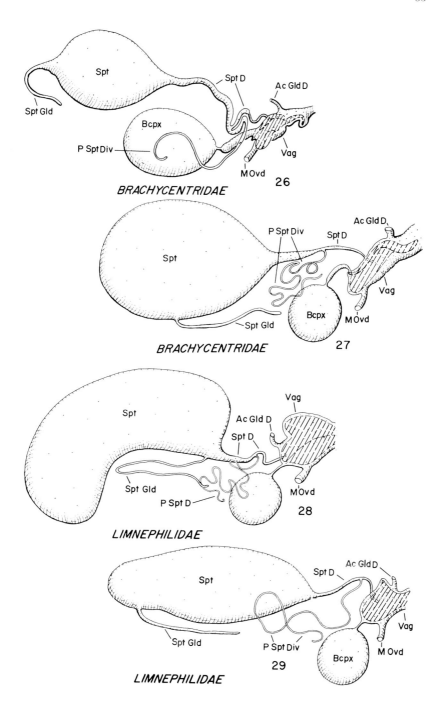

BRACHYCENTRIDAE 26

BRACHYCENTRIDAE 27

LIMNEPHILIDAE 28

LIMNEPHILIDAE 29

PLATE 9

Fig. 30. Limnephilidae, *Pycnopsyche subfasciata*, left lateral aspect of female genitalia.

Fig. 31. Limnephilidae, *Radema stigmatella*, left lateral aspect of female genitalia.

Fig. 32. Goeridae, *Goera calcarata*, A: left lateral aspect of female genitalia, B: dorsal aspect of spermathecal duct showing sclerotized ring.

Fig. 33. Goeridae, *Goerita genota*, left lateral aspect of female genitalia.

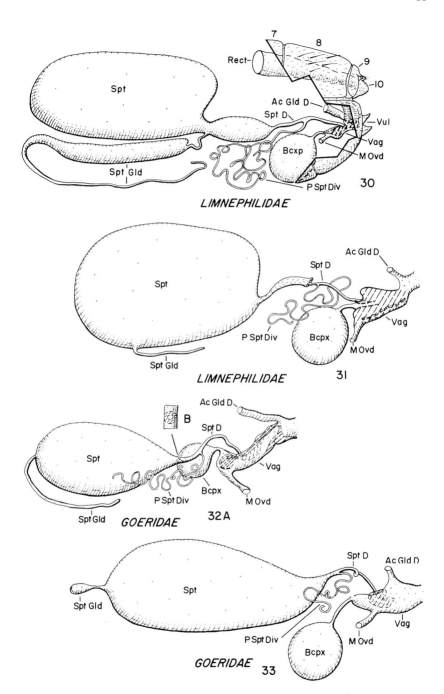

LIMNEPHILIDAE 30

LIMNEPHILIDAE 31

GOERIDAE 32 A

GOERIDAE 33

PLATE 10

Fig. 34. Plectrotarsidae, *Plectrotarsus gravenhorstii*, left lateral aspect of female genitalia.

Fig. 35. Phryganeidae, *Phryganea cinerea*, left lateral aspect of female genitalia.

Fig. 36. Phryganeidae, *Yphria californica*, left lateral aspect of female genitalia.

Fig. 37. Limnocentropodidae, *Limnocentropus* sp., left lateral aspect of female genitalia.

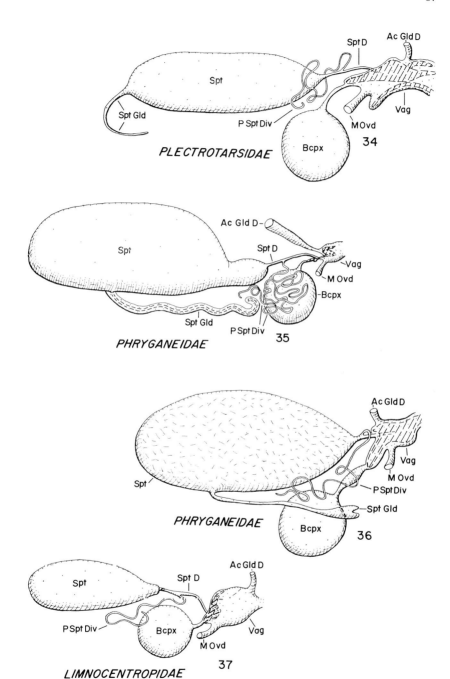

PLECTROTARSIDAE 34

PHRYGANEIDAE 35

PHRYGANEIDAE 36

LIMNOCENTROPIDAE 37

PLATE 11

Fig. 38. Beraeidae, *Beraea fontana*, left lateral aspect of female genitalia.

Fig. 39. Sericostomatidae, *Sericostoma personata*, A: left lateral aspect of female genitalia, B: dorsal aspect of sclerotized plates in accessory gland duct.

Fig. 40. Pycnocentrellidae, *Pycnocentrella eruensis*, left lateral aspect of female genitalia.

Fig. 41. Lepidostomatidae, *Oeconesus maori*, left lateral aspect of female genitalia.

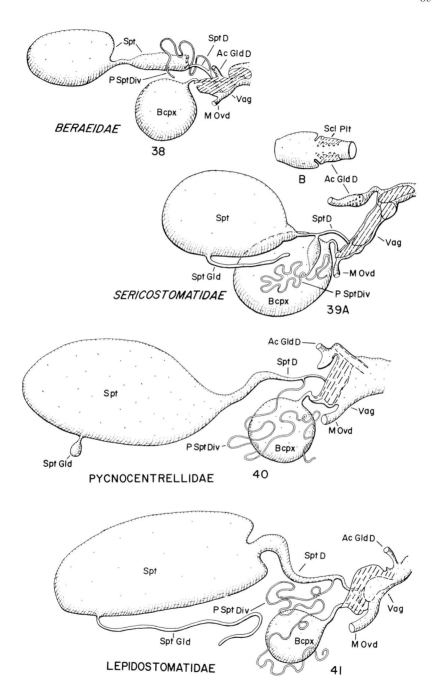

BERAEIDAE 38

B

SERICOSTOMATIDAE 39A

PYCNOCENTRELLIDAE 40

LEPIDOSTOMATIDAE 41

PLATE 12

Fig. 42. Sericostomatidae, *Olinga feredyi*, left lateral aspect of female genitalia.
Fig. 43. Sericostomatidae, *Beraeoptera roria*, left lateral aspect of female genitalia.
Fig. 44. Odontoceridae, *Marilia flexuosa*, left lateral aspect of female genitalia.
Fig. 45. Molannidae, *Molanna uniophila*, left lateral aspect of female genitalia.

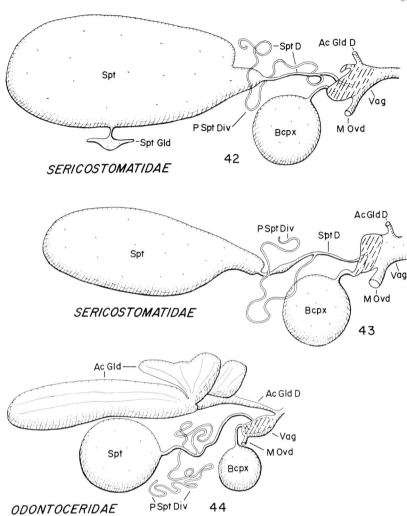

SERICOSTOMATIDAE 42

SERICOSTOMATIDAE 43

ODONTOCERIDAE 44

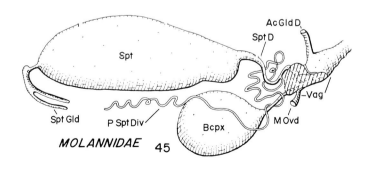

MOLANNIDAE 45

PLATE 13

Fig. 46. Calamoceratidae, *Anisocentropus pyraloides*, left lateral aspect of female genitalia.

Fig. 47. Calamoceratidae, *Notiomyia* sp., left lateral aspect of female genitalia.

Fig. 48. Helicopsychidae, *Helicopsyche borealis*, left lateral aspect of female genitalia.

Fig. 49. Leptoceridae, *Triaenodes florida*, left lateral aspect of female genitalia.

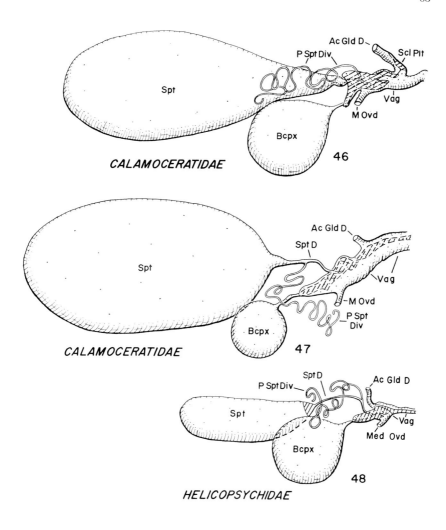

CALAMOCERATIDAE 46

CALAMOCERATIDAE 47

HELICOPSYCHIDAE 48

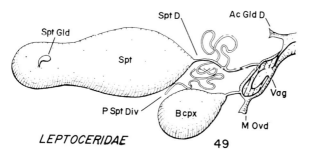

LEPTOCERIDAE 49

PLATE 14

Fig. 50. Phylogenetic diagram of the Trichoptera (modified from Ross, 1967).

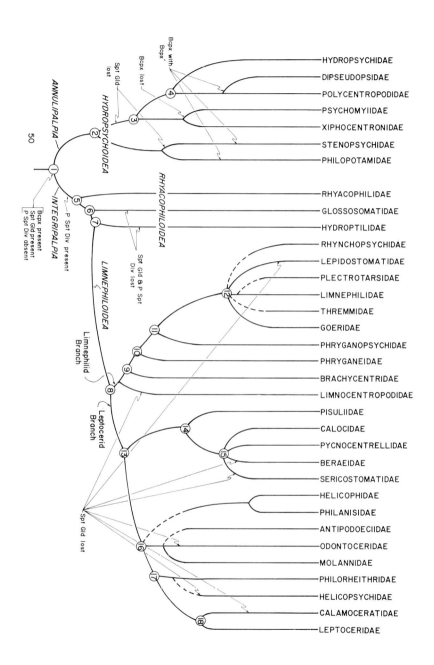

ANNULIPALPIA

HYDROPSYCHOIDEA

Bcpx with Bcpx

Bcpx lost

Spt Gld lost

② ③ ④

HYDROPSYCHIDAE
DIPSEUDOPSIDAE
POLYCENTROPODIDAE
PSYCHOMYIIDAE
XIPHOCENTRONIDAE
STENOPSYCHIDAE
PHILOPOTAMIDAE

50

①

INTEGRIPALPIA

Bcpx present
Spt Gld present
P Spt Div absent

P Spt Div present

⑤ ⑥ ⑦

RHYACOPHILOIDEA

Spt Gld & P Spt Div lost

RHYACOPHILIDAE
GLOSSOSOMATIDAE
HYDROPTILIDAE

LIMNEPHILOIDEA

Limnephilid Branch

⑪ ⑫

RHYNCHOPSYCHIDAE
LEPIDOSTOMATIDAE
PLECTROTARSIDAE
LIMNEPHILIDAE
THREMMIDAE
GOERIDAE

⑩ ⑨ ⑧

PHRYGANOPSYCHIDAE
PHRYGANEIDAE
BRACHYCENTRIDAE
LIMNOCENTROPODIDAE

Leptocerid Branch

⑬ ⑭ ⑮

PISULIIDAE
CALOCIDAE
PYCNOCENTRELLIDAE
BERAEIDAE
SERICOSTOMATIDAE

Spt Gld lost

⑯

HELICOPHIDAE
PHILANISIDAE
ANTIPODOECIIDAE
ODONTOCERIDAE
MOLANNIDAE

⑰

PHILORHEITHRIDAE
HELICOPSYCHIDAE

⑱

CALAMOCERATIDAE
LEPTOCERIDAE

INDEX